Ben's Brilliant Birthday

Damian Harvey
Illustrated by Justine Dowling

RIGBY

It was Ben's birthday.
He got lots of presents.

3

In the first present, he got a bus.

To Ben from Josh

In the second present, he got a ball.

To Ben
From Auntie Ann

In the third present, he got a bat.

In the fourth present, he got a book.

In the fifth present, he got a boomerang.

12

13

In the sixth present, he got a bell . . .

Love, Mum and Dad

for a bicycle!
"Brilliant!" said Ben.

Happy Birthday!
Love, Mum and Dad